# Dundee Royal Infirmary

*a history in old photographs*

Dr Graham Lowe

This 1796 promotional halfpenny for Dundee's Infirmary was designed by local coin-maker James Wright Jnr. It depicts the Infirmary complete with its intended extensions, though these would not materialise until the 1820s.

Text © Dr Graham Lowe, 2018.
First published in the United Kingdom, 2018,
by Stenlake Publishing Ltd.
Telephone: 01290 551122
www.stenlake.co.uk

Printed by Berforts, 17 Burgess Road, Hastings, TN35 4NR

ISBN 9781840338232

**The publishers regret that they cannot supply
copies of any pictures featured in this book.**

# Acknowledgements

Grateful thanks are due to Keith Baxby, Bill Morrison, Howard Stevenson, Alistair Swanson and Avril Watchorn for help with the text, and Matthew Jarron of the University of Dundee Museum Services for providing the images, all of which are from the collections of the Tayside Medical History Museum. We have made attempts to trace copyright holders but should any permission have been overlooked please let us know and we can amend any subsequent editions of the book.

It is hoped that this book will help to complement the earlier publications on DRI by Henry Gibson (1948) and Norman Watson (1998).

# Introduction

Early hospitals in Scotland were designed to treat with rest and spiritual support rather than acute illness, and the first that we would recognise as such came as a result of the voluntary hospital movement which gradually gained momentum in the 18th century, often preceded by out-patient dispensaries. This local charity for the poor arose from an intricate combination of factors, different parts of the country having their own particular driving force of necessity, socio-economic pressure or charitable intent. Inter-civic rivalry and the dominance of towns over their hinterlands would also have been strong factors in determining their advent. Fundraising came in many forms from wealthy benefactors, subscribers, church collections, all manner of social events, and with particular support from the working class who had their own self-help ethos stimulated by dangerous work conditions of the time. In a voluntary hospital the visiting surgeons and physicians gave their services for free or for a nominal sum, earning their livelihoods in general or private practice outside the hospital.

This book gives a glimpse into the life and times of Dundee Royal Infirmary, or DRI as it was fondly known. The hospital existed for 200 years from 1798 until 1998, and was preceded by a dispensary for out-patient treatment from 1735. Both were of charitable intent prior to the National Health Service taking over in 1948, and were dependent on sufficient money forthcoming to provide the necessary care required. In the early days of the Infirmary, wealthy people were able to summon medical and surgical care to their own homes, and it was not until antiseptic / aseptic measures were put in place to make surgery safer and anaesthetics were discovered to make it pain-free that the more affluent changed from home to hospital for their care. With evolving diagnostic and therapeutic advances, inevitably costs rose, putting extra strain on the available funds, and Dundee was lucky to have some wealthy philanthropists to help out when need arose.

The Infirmary was often under pressure to accommodate patients requiring attention, particularly when epidemic fevers reared their heads in the 19th century, and sometimes directors had to vacate their committee room and surgeons their theatre to find room for them all. What a relief it must have been when Kings Cross Hospital was eventually built in 1889, probably 40 years after it should have been. Royal Victoria Hospital opened in 1899 and would have been another blessing as it removed the 'bed-blockers' of the day – patients with 'incurable' conditions such as cancer, paralysis and rheumatism. And from 1890 the Eastern Hospital was run in association with the neighbouring Poorhouse, later becoming Maryfield Hospital which gradually lost its Poor Law image as its services were upgraded.

For the last 25 years of its existence, DRI lived harmoniously alongside the brand new Ninewells Hospital, but it was inevitable that at some stage the two would have to combine, particularly from the point of view of the Accident & Emergency and Intensive Care services. A&E was run quite differently in the days before the ready access to CAT scans and other sophisticated diagnostic and therapeutic techniques that we often take for granted today. Whether phase two of the DRI transfer should have taken place earlier, however, is a matter of debate not to be discussed here!

Dr Graham Lowe

Dr Graham Lowe is a retired Consultant Dermatologist at NHS Tayside and former Honorary Curator of Tayside Medical History Museum. He worked in several departments of Dundee Royal Infirmary during his career and cared for it deeply.

Situated between King Street and Victoria Road and costing £1,400 to build, the first 56-bed Dundee Infirmary served the needs of the community of Dundee and its environs from 1798 until 1855; there was a two-year wait at the start while £308 was raised to equip the Infirmary. Initially, there were seven visiting surgeons who took charge of all the patients in rotation for a month at a time and performed any operations that were needed during that period; two attending physicians who had light duties; and a resident apothecary in addition to a housekeeper-matron and one or two nurses. In the early days, patients bearing with them a Governor's letter of recommendation were admitted at the discretion of the visiting surgeon each Thursday morning, with special allowance being made for those who had come from a distance, who had met with an accident requiring immediate aid, or who were labouring under a contagious fever. Emergency patients were admitted free, otherwise the Governor met the boarding fee of 3/6d per week; gradually, as funds allowed, more patients were allowed free accommodation. The directors enforced a code of discipline for staff and patients, so that nurses were not to neglect, insult or quarrel with patients, and patients were not allowed to smoke in the wards or play cards or dice. The hospital became Dundee Royal Infirmary in 1819 by Royal Charter and extensions were later added on each side to raise the bed complement to 120. This engraving by William Young shows the building before the extensions were added. It was first published in *Dundee Delineated* (1822).

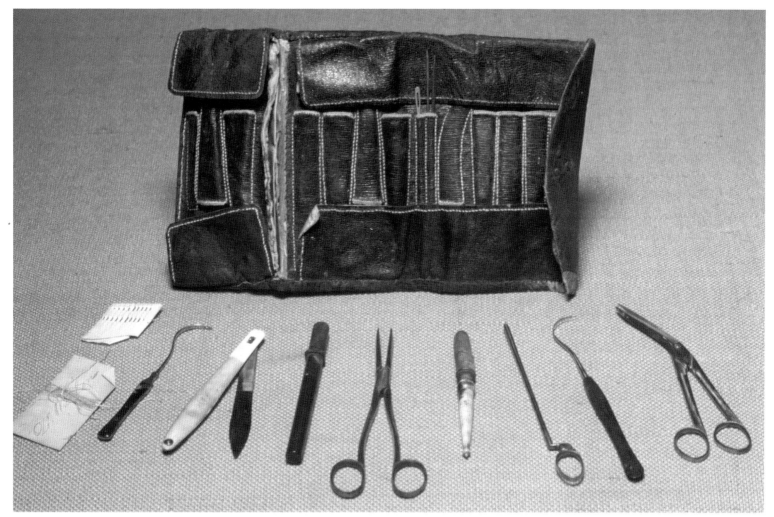

This instrument case made of soft black leather contains lancets, knives, probes, forceps, artery hooks, needles and thread. Bone and ivory handles were a relic of pre-aseptic surgery days before stainless steel took over. The case belonged to Andrew Willison who was one of the first attending surgeons at Dundee Infirmary, where he served from 1798 to 1822. Before the advent of effective anaesthesia in the 1840s, surgical procedures were limited mainly to surface lesions, industrial accidents and lithotomy, and around 25 a year were carried out at DRI.

*Right*: Born in Dundee, John Crichton set up practice in the Overgate after obtaining the diploma of the College of Surgeons in Edinburgh. He was one of the original attending surgeons appointed to the Dundee Infirmary when it opened in 1798, working there until 1855 when the new Royal Infirmary opened. He was known as one of the most skilled surgeons of his day, in particular for his speciality of lithotomy to remove stones from the bladder; patients came to him from far and wide and his mortality rate of less than 7% of over 200 of these operations was remarkable in the days before effective anaesthesia and antisepsis. He attributed his success to "the happiness of a mind that was never ruffled or disconcerted, and a hand that never trembled". Happily married for 61 years, he was a faithful member of the Glasite church. Crichton Street was named after his family in compensation for losing their home to this new road linking the High Street to the harbour. This portrait was painted by John Gibson in 1841 and hung in the boardroom of DRI until its closure.

*Above*: Born in Cupar, Alexander Bell was a general practitioner in Dundee for 43 years, and also served as attending surgeon at DRI from 1807-37. In 1816 he was responsible for ordering "good surgical instruments" for the Infirmary. He was an early proponent of vaccination against smallpox, which was introduced by Edward Jenner in 1798. He had witnessed the failure of variolation (inoculating scratched skin with smallpox pus from a mild case in an attempt to induce immunity) during his training, and as it was a controversial and dangerous practice, variolation was made illegal in the UK in 1840. This portrait was painted by local artist John Stewart around 1852.

*Above*: This simple stethoscope which has become the hallmark of physicians was actually made by its 1816 inventor René Laennec, who had felt uncomfortable placing his ear on women's chests to hear heart sounds. He gave it to William Sharpey of Arbroath who became Professor of Physiology in London, and he gave it in turn to his half-brother, James Arrott, who worked at DRI from 1833-55 and who set up the first clinic in Dundee for studying chest diseases at the Watt Institute. Stethoscope design later evolved into the binaural instrument we are all familiar with today, invented in 1851.

*Right*: General anaesthetics reached DRI in 1847, soon after ether's world launch. Dr Munro recorded "After taking charge of the surgical wards on the 1st of June 1847, I resolved to take every opportunity of testing the efficacy of the anaesthetic properties of ether and chloroform … at that time ether only was in use, and the first operation we had to perform was lithotomy … success was most perfect and pleasing … several other operations and always with similar results … [Ether] soon became superseded by chloroform, which is less irritating and more pleasant to inhale … is more certain and persistent in its effects … in every instance complete insensibility to pain has been the result and without any bad effect having been observed to follow its use". Because of the risk of infection however, it was only when Lister's 1867 antiseptic (carbolic acid), and later aseptic (sterilised instruments, clean hands, gowns, gloves, masks) measures were introduced that the number of annual operations performed at DRI substantially increased from about 25 to 100 by 1871, and to 1,000 by the end of the century. Seen here are an early mask and ether bottle.

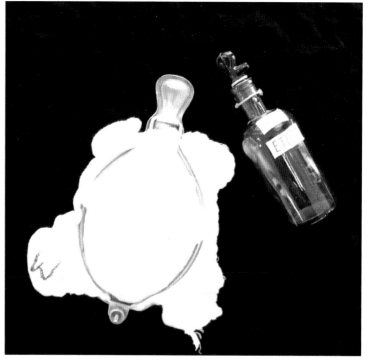

By the mid-19th century the combination of rapid rise in population and inadequate bed space to house epidemics made it clear that some form of hospital expansion was required. The question of enlarging the present building or building on a new site was put in the hands of Edinburgh professors Christison and Syme, and they came down on the side of a new build. The new DRI Foundation Stone ceremony in 1852 was a memorable occasion, a complete holiday in beautiful weather. A large procession wended its way from the Royal Arch up through Castle Street, High Street, Reform Street and Constitution Road to the new Infirmary site. The Duke of Atholl laid the stone with full Masonic honours. Within its hollow lay a glass vase with the lithograph reproduced here arranged around its inner side, together with a number of dispensary documents, publications and artefacts of the time. The vase was carefully placed by an old mason into a block from a local quarry, not from the Normandy stone that had been imported to face the building – "Na, na, we'el nae trust it in the heart of a Frenchman, we maun pit it intae a native", he is reputed to have said. He was right, for the facing Normandy stone around the windows did not stand up to the Scots climate and had to be replaced within 30 years at the considerable cost of about £5,000.

The son of a Dundee surgeon and chemist, Dr David Greig had a distinguished undergraduate career at Edinburgh University. Along with two other young surgeons, he was sent by Professors Simpson and Syme to the Crimea to show how chloroform should be used. He sailed on the same ship as Florence Nightingale and served with her at Scutari. There he had to bury his Edinburgh colleagues who had succumbed to typhus, only narrowly recovering from the same illness himself. He went on to serve as one of the surgeons of the 17th Regiment of Foot until the end of the war and was awarded the Turkish and Crimean medals. On his return to this country, he served as surgeon at DRI from 1859-90. His son, David Middleton Greig, was also a surgeon.

Blood-letting of patients with inflammation or deep-seated pain believed to be due to an imbalance of the humors (blood, phlegm and yellow and black bile) was a frequent treatment for millennia up until the end of the 19th century, and the art of cupping with blood-letting was a skill which Victorian surgeons and physicians acquired. The air inside the cup was warmed by means of a flaming stick and the cup was applied to the skin. As the air cooled the skin was drawn into the cup as a swelling, stopping the flow of blood. The scarificator was then applied immediately, and the lancets contained within were triggered by a lever to bleed the skin. The cup could then be reapplied to collect the blood. The same treatment without the bleeding is called dry cupping which is still used, outwith the NHS. This set belonged to Dr James Christie who was a physician at DRI from 1856-84.

Another way of extracting blood from patients in the 19th century was by means of lancets or fleams, and secure cases for these became popular gifts for physicians and surgeons. Double-edged lancets were extremely sharp, and here the blades were shielded by tortoiseshell which folded back to be used as handles. This case was given by the widow of Dr John Glen to Dr William Crockett, a physician at DRI. Dr Glen was resident medical superintendent at DRI until his untimely death in 1863 from typhus. In this six month period, two other DRI superintendents and a matron also died of typhus.

*Above left*: An important event occurred at DRI in 1874 with the arrival as matron of Rebecca Strong from St Thomas' Hospital in London, where she had been a pupil of Florence Nightingale. Dr Robert Sinclair had presented a comprehensive report on the unsatisfactory state of the nursing department, particularly the night staff, recommending that a training school for young women of good character and education be established under the control of a qualified and efficient matron. His proposals were immediately endorsed by the directors and over the next five years Mrs Strong and Dr Sinclair raised the nursing department to a standard that was exceptionally high for the time. Mrs Strong later moved on to Glasgow, where she had more difficulty implementing her reforms, but went on to become an international figure in nursing circles and was awarded the OBE.

*Above right*: The Dalgleish Nurses' Home was opened in 1896, able to accommodate 40 nurses. The cost of £4,000 was borne by Sir William Ogilvy Dalgleish, the President of the Infirmary. Nursing had become a popular profession, as evidenced by a rapid rise in the number of applicants to the training school, and the home was extended in 1912 to help house these new nurses. In later years, it was the venue for many a late-night party, but it also had a more relaxing piano with which to entertain guests.

This 1897 photograph of the 'Electrical Room' at DRI shows early x-ray apparatus used by Dr George Pirie, just over a year after their discovery by Wilhelm Röntgen in Würzberg, now one of Dundee's twin-cities. They were called x-rays as Röntgen knew so little about them, 'x' being the unknown quantity in mathematics. The apparatus includes an induction coil to provide an electric charge to the evacuated electrode-containing tube, which would generate the x-rays.

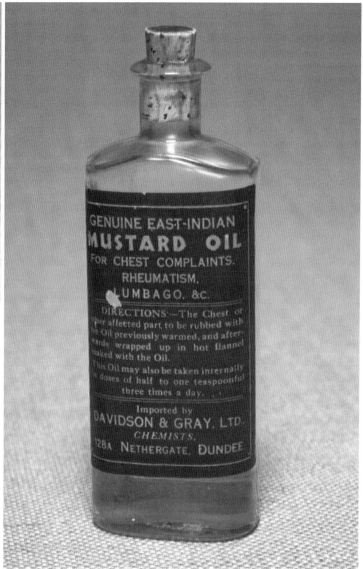

In the early days of x-ray use, Dr Pirie found it useful to test how strong the rays were using the fluoroscope shown above. He would place the device near the x-ray tube, apply the electric current, and then hold his hand between the tube and the fluorescent plate of the fluoroscope; the clarity of the image of the bones in his hand on the screen was proportional to the strength of the x-rays. Unfortunately, he was unaware of the dangers of this practice. The first sign of damage to the skin of Pirie's hands was a sensation of tingling, itchiness and pain. Soothing preparations like this mustard oil were used to try to reduce the discomfort, but these symptoms were followed by the development of tumours which ultimately caused both hands to be amputated. Despite using protective goggles, his eyesight also began to fail and he had to retire in 1925. Pirie was awarded a Carnegie Hero Trust medal and pension for his brave endeavours, and his name is included on a memorial to early x-ray pioneers in Hamburg.

This view of the DRI pharmacy at the turn of the 20th century shows lots of bottles and jars of medicines lining the shelves, and various measuring cylinders on the table. Each ward had a basket to transport the medicines, which would probably have had limited effect in relieving the patients' symptoms.

In 1902, jute-mill owner James Caird offered DRI Directors £18,500 to erect a hospital for the treatment of cancer along with £5,000 running costs to fund research, and it opened four years later. Dr Archibald Leitch from Rothesay was appointed investigator in cancer research, having previously worked in the cancer research laboratories of Middlesex Hospital. A year on, DRI's Annual Report noted the "wide field which has to be gone over and the difficulties which have to be overcome before a definite statement may be made as to the nature of the disease". No further funds for research were forthcoming when Caird's money ran out, so Leitch moved back to London and the six wards and two operating theatres soon ceased to specialise.

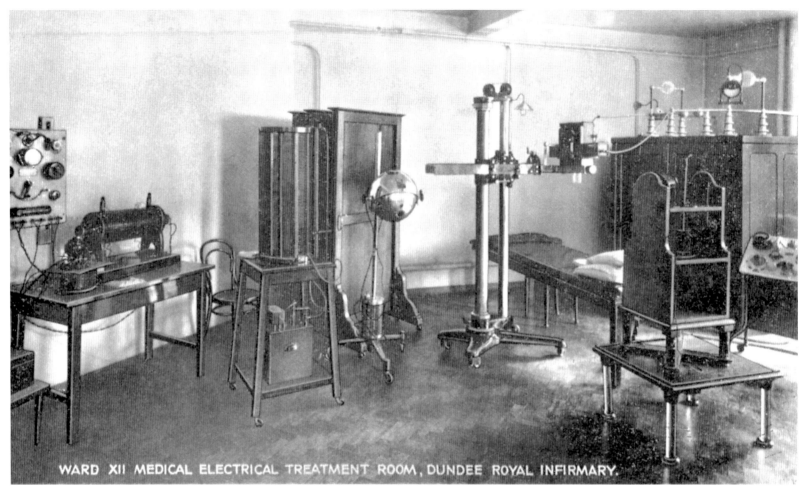

**WARD XII MEDICAL ELECTRICAL TREATMENT ROOM, DUNDEE ROYAL INFIRMARY.**

The early 20th century heralded an age of electro-optimism when all manner of ailments were claimed to be amenable to electrical therapy. Some of the claims such as the electrified penis to "modernise masculinity" were nothing short of quackery, but plenty of patients with certain forms of neurological, muscular and connective tissue disease regularly attended DRI for treatment. One of the wards in the Caird Cancer Hospital was fitted up with electrical apparatus to treat superficial forms of cancer, tuberculosis of the skin and other skin diseases. In total there were more than 10,000 out-patient visits each year for this form of treatment, not unusual in those days. The emergence of DIY brain stimulation and EEG headsets marketed for gaming, brain training and meditation indicate a modern revival where, just as it was 100 years ago, the hope and the hype could be hard to disentangle.

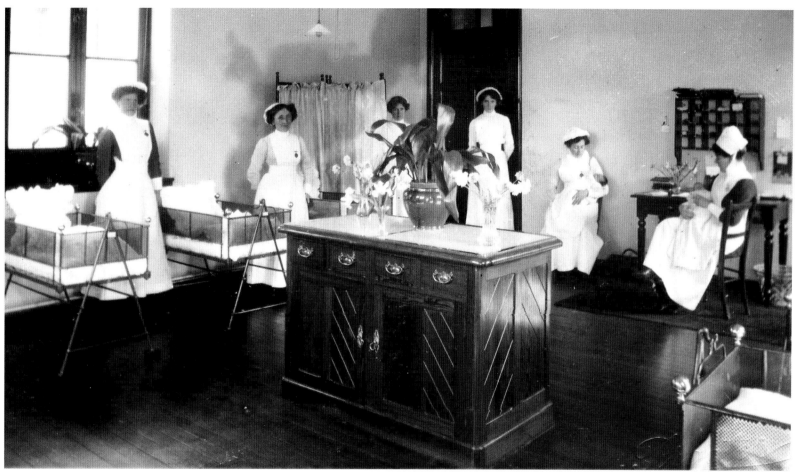

In 1899 a maternity hospital paid for by Sir James Caird was erected at DRI. It was sorely needed because of high maternal and infant mortality; a typical year in 1913 showed that out of 207 deliveries, 33 children were stillborn, a further eighteen died soon after birth and twelve mothers also died from complications of childbirth. By the mid-1920s it had become clear that this hospital was quite inadequate for the increasing demand; a decision was made to build a new maternity hospital in 1930, and the entire cost of £30,000 was met by members of the Sharp jute family of Hill of Tarvit in Fife. By this time only women expecting their first babies were admitted unless complications were anticipated. The maternity nurses not only worked in the hospital, but were also sent out to deliveries on the district; they could travel free on the trams when visiting outdoor patients, courtesy of the Town Council. This photograph shows the original Caird maternity ward of 1899.

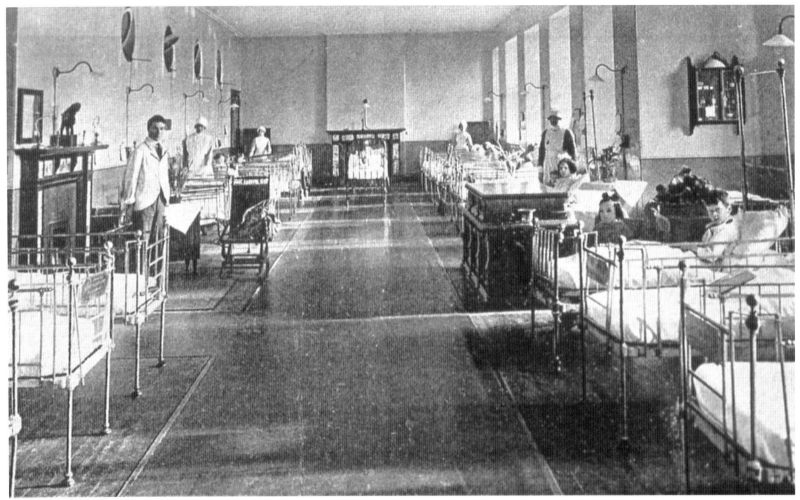

Edinburgh, Glasgow and Aberdeen had all opened Royal Hospitals for Sick Children by 1882, but Tayside children were cared for in the regional voluntary hospitals. At DRI the first ward for children appeared in 1883, and two others followed in 1915 and 1927. Dundee's first paediatrician from 1907 was Dr J S Y Rogers who had a broad Scots accent and a powerful personality. To his mind childhood diseases would never be thoroughly attended to until there was a properly equipped children's hospital, for which he long campaigned; the outbreak of the First World War caused plans for a 100-bed hospital to be shelved, and it took until 2006 for a separate Children's Hospital to come about at Ninewells. Shown here is a children's ward from the 1920s.

*Right*: Brass plaques fixed above the DRI beds and cots celebrated endowments and naming made by members of the public; the benefactor(s) might be an individual, a group of people or a whole institution – three examples are shown here. The money from these plaques at 1,000 guineas a time for bed/cot endowments and 200 guineas for bed/cot naming was channelled into an endowment fund, only the interest of which was used for current expenses; this fund stood at £520,000 when the National Health Service took over the Infirmary. There was also a reserve fund made up from legacies and larger donations to pay off debt when expenditure exceeded income.

*Above*: This exclusive badge was issued to those who collected at least 3 lbs of silver paper, the proceeds of which went to the Children's Department at DRI. 809 individuals and groups such as schools, churches and guides were registered as members. In 1928 13,158 lbs of silver paper raised £315.

Wealthy philanthropists like Sir James Caird and his sister Mrs Emma Marryat repeatedly came to the rescue of DRI, both from capital projects such as the Caird Cancer Hospital (the Caird block) and Marryat operating theatres, as well as running costs of the hospital; on her death in 1927, half the residue of Mrs Marryat's estate amounting to £120,000 was bequeathed to the Infirmary. Donations were continually sought in other ways such as the University Students Charities Campaign, Hospital Sunday (when all the city church collections went to the local hospitals) and an annual Butchers v Ministers football match. Seen here are an early collection tin and a photograph of Dundee students collecting around 1927.

These genito-urinary instruments belonged to Lloyd Turton Price, who was appointed Professor of Surgery in 1920. He was noted for his clinical teaching, high clinical standards and sympathetic bedside manner, especially with young children. He died in 1933 following an operation in Edinburgh for duodenal ulcer, when his wound burst open from coughing and was complicated by pneumonia. 2,000 mourners are said to have turned up in pouring rain to pay their last respects at his funeral in the Western Cemetery. In his will, he bequeathed his whole estate to the gynaecologist Margaret Fairlie, whom he had planned to marry.

This cystoscope for examining the bladder was used by Frank Brown who was appointed to the surgical department at DRI in 1921. A heavy smoker, he was known to discard the last pre-operative cigarette after cleaning his hands with spirit at the end of the scrub-up. At the operating table itself, however, he was in the words of his colleague Stanley Souter "a supreme technician, unhurried and unruffled, bringing to each operation … scrupulous skill and delicate touch". Earlier, he had seen distinguished service as a Major in the First World War, earning the military OBE. Devoted to country pursuits, a favourite story of his concerned a famous neurosurgeon who was having an off-day shooting, the keeper noting "huh, weel, he's nae damned idea where a pheasant has *its* brains"!

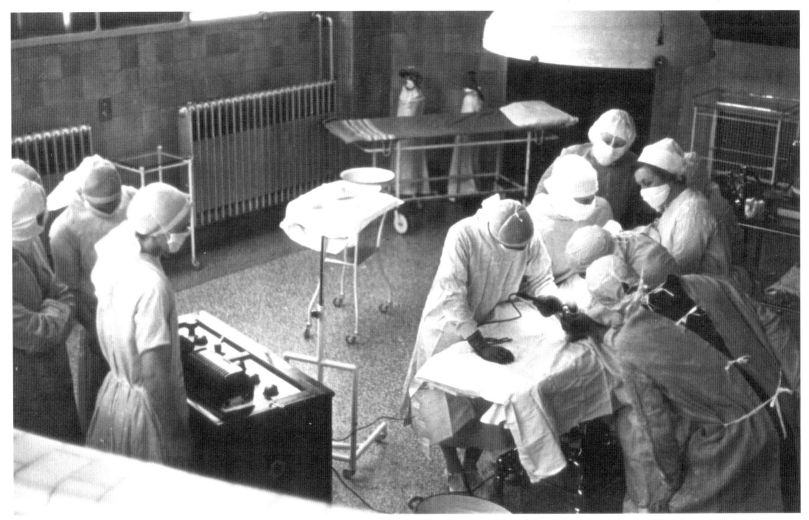

The advent of asepsis to prevent infection led to better design of operating theatres, equipment and clothing. All contents of the theatre had to be easily washable, window frames were flush with the inner surface of walls, angles were rounded, instruments with bone or ivory handles gave way to solid forged tools, surgeons replaced frock coats with theatre gowns and all staff washed their hands and wore gloves and masks. Instruments were sterilised in an autoclave in theatre and hand-picked by the nurse-in-charge before the operation. This photograph shows an operation in the Caird Block in the 1930s.

**Dundee Royal Infirmary.**

ADMIT BEARER TO WARD 2 ONLY.

To Visit *Patrick Fitzsimmons*

On SUNDAYS,       2 to 2.30 p.m.
     TUESDAYS,       2 to 2.30 ,,
     THURSDAYS,       2 to 2.30 ,,
     and SATURDAYS, -       4 to 4.30 ,,

This Ticket must be shown to the PORTER and the NURSE at each visit.

Week-day visitors may bring with them flowers, a toy, a fresh egg, a plain biscuit, or an orange, which must be handed to the Nurse. No pastry, jelly, sugar, nor anything sticky, and no spirits or wine of any kind is permitted, and on Sundays nothing except flowers.

Visitors must be orderly and quiet in the Wards and Corridors, and are not allowed to sit on the beds, or put their clothes upon them.

By order of the Directors,
H. E. FRASER, M.D.,
*Medical Superintendent.*

Date, 5/9/10

Visiting time in DRI used to be very strict, and limited to one hour for two visitors. The two cards issued for each patient had to be registered and deposited at the main front door before progressing along the corridors to the designated ward. If there were more than two visitors to a patient, they had to go in relays, returning to the door and exchanging cards, all of which took up some of the allotted hour. As seen from the earlier card here, visiting hours were even more stringent in 1910. The patient referred to, Patrick Fitzsimmons, recovered from his illness but was one of many Dundonians who lost his life at the Battle of Loos five years later.

Form 17.

**Dundee Royal Infirmary.**

**1931**

ADMIT BEARER TO VISIT

Patient *Amelia Robertson* in Ward 7

On SUNDAYS       - from 2 to 3 p.m.
TUESDAYS and THURSDAYS - ,, 5.30 to 6.30 ,,
WEDNESDAYS and SATURDAYS ,, 3 to 4 ,,

Date 11/4/31       By Order of the Directors.

Your attention is directed to the Rules on the Other Side of this Card.

18,000-f-1/31.

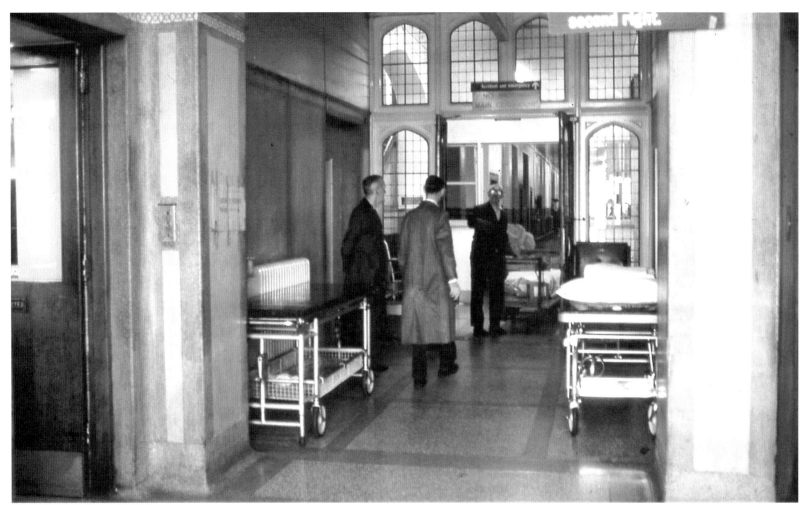

D M Brown owned a large department store at the junction of Commercial Street and the High Street, a landmark for many generations of Dundee's citizens. He served as a DRI director for twelve years and later as a vice-president. His outstanding gift to the Infirmary was the reconstruction of the main ground floor corridor (seen here) in 1928, the floor of which was lined with hygienic impervious terrazzo. It also incorporated a mosaic with the city's coat of arms and the hospital's motto *Pro aegris et laesis* – 'for the sick and injured' (see inside front cover). The West Door was also enlarged to allow for more convenient handling of patients.

*Left*: Known universally to colleagues and students as 'Madam', Margaret Fairlie inspired feelings of respect tinged with awe in those around her. She became the first woman to hold a Chair in a Scottish university when appointed Professor of Obstetrics & Gynaecology in 1940; she was greeted at the time by the Professor of Medicine Adam Patrick with the palindrome "Madam, I'm Adam"! After a visit to the Marie Curie Foundation in Paris she pioneered radium treatment for gynaecological cancer, and for many years ran a weekly follow-up radium clinic. She also developed vaginal smear cytology for cancer diagnosis. Although said to operate "like a man", on one occasion to the amusement of students in the operating theatre, her pink underskirt descended slowly below her gown until it lay around her ankles; ignoring it until the end of the operation, she then stepped out of it, picked it up and walked out of theatre without batting an eyelid!

*Right*: Alexander Fleming's accidental discovery in London of the antibacterial action of penicillium mould in 1928 has become part of medical folklore. It was more than ten years later however that Florey and Chain took this further and produced therapeutic penicillin in 1941, initially in America where facilities for production were better. Penicillin was only given at first to casualties of war, and it was November 1944 before a mother with puerperal fever was treated in Dundee. The surgeon Stanley Soutar at DRI had to take a special course of instruction before he could prescribe penicillin; as most local surgeons were on active service, Mr Soutar was on constant call and performed all emergency operations, except when relieved on Tuesdays and Fridays from 2-10pm! This bottle of yellow powder contains the calcium salt of penicillin, used in DRI in 1946, the yellow colour being due to impurities; it would take a long time to dissolve the powder in water prior to injection.

Before the Second World War, the approach to and treatment of heart disease was very limited. That was to change dramatically in 1951 with the appointments of the already-distinguished Ian Hill (left) and Donald Douglas (right) as the first full-time Professors of Medicine and Surgery in Dundee. These driving personalities collaborated closely in the care of cardiac patients, and went on to transform their departments into dynamic academic units, achieving national and international recognition. They also became respectively Honorary Physician and Surgeon to the Queen in Scotland. It was to be a golden period with DRI right at the cutting edge of advances in modern cardiology.

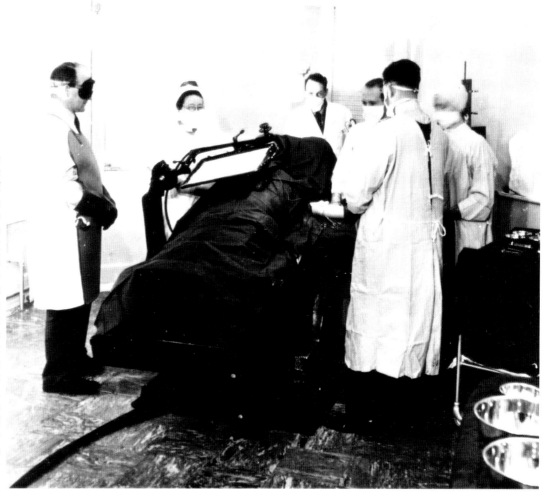

A native of Arbroath, after the war Ken Lowe worked on the first kidney dialysis machine at the premier research establishment of Hammersmith Hospital in London where he acquired expertise in passing a catheter into the heart (cardiac catheterisation) to measure pressure and oxygen concentration. This skill attracted him to Professor Ian Hill at DRI, and he came north to initiate a research team with Dr Donald Emslie-Smith and Dr Hamish Watson that over the next fifteen years investigated a number of heart disorders with this new technique. This work culminated in the discovery of conduction along an important nerve bundle that triggered further study in the USA, which in time led on to ablative treatment of heart rhythm disorders. In this photograph, Dr Lowe is in the centre, with Professor Hill's dominating shadow on the left side; the top of his head can just be seen behind the nurse. Dr Lowe became an Honorary Professor at a time when few existed, and was also Honorary Physician to the Queen in Scotland.

This looks like it is visiting time at the DRI with the traffic policeman making sure that the vehicles proceed in an orderly manner. You can just see on the right side of this 1954 photograph that there was a covered walkway, later removed, leading from the lodge up to the main door.

Dr J F Riley was a surgeon during the war but switched to radiotherapy after contracting a skin condition of his hands that prevented him from operating. Riley had always been fascinated by research and the great heroes of the past such as the German Paul Ehrlich who had discovered mast cells in humans, although not solved the riddle of what they do. Riley set out to solve this riddle, and made a good start with a notable series of experiments conducted during the 1950s in a corner of his room at DRI. He teamed up with pharmacologist Geoffrey West to establish the mast cell granule as the major source of histamine, a fundamental contribution to the understanding of inflammatory and allergic reactions, earning him international recognition. Here we see Dr Riley and some of his experimental equipment.

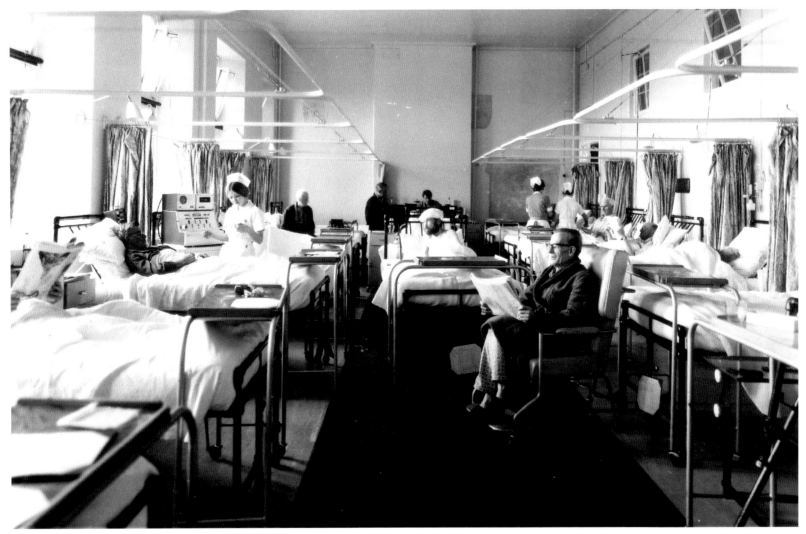

DRI and Maryfield used to alternate admission days, and if all the beds became occupied extra ones were simply added down the middle of the ward. The lack of privacy and bed curtains were very inconvenient and the poor staff must surely have been run off their feet, if it was possible to run in the cramped conditions. This is Ward 4 photographed in 1970.

Just as an army marches on its stomach, so do hospital staff, and DRI always provided the best of sustenance in a convivial atmosphere just off Wards 8 and 9. In a previous era, doctors were given meals in their own Gilroy retreat where snooker was a competitive post-prandial pursuit, but they later came to join their essential ancillary staff in the main canteen.

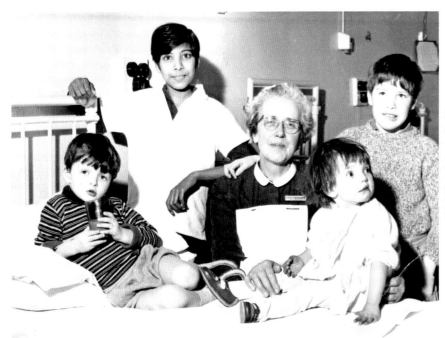

Sister Alison Kiddie was a much-loved member of staff at DRI, serving as ward sister to the eye unit from the Second World War until retiral in 1976 . She had an uncanny ability to remember all her patients and their families, to whom she was a constant source of kindness and comfort. This unfailing caring devotion allied to her exceptional professional skills were recognised by her being made Dundee's Citizen of the Year in 1972. She grew up in Arbroath with her younger brother, the aforementioned Dr Kenneth Lowe.

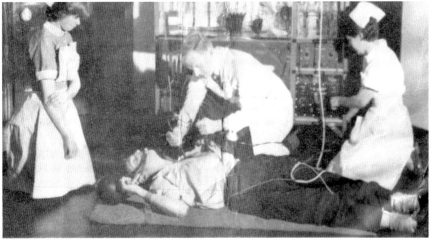

Medical and nursing staff were being made aware of cardiac arrest procedure around the same time as the popular drama *Emergency – Ward 10* was being aired on television. Before 1960, if a heart attack patient suffered a cardiac arrest, he or she was simply left to recover or not, but around that time it was realised that some patients could be brought back from the brink of death by using fairly simple procedures and drugs. This photograph is from a pamphlet devised by Dr WK Stewart to educate staff on how to save lives, and shows DRI's first cardiac arrest trolley in simulated action. In 1964, Dr Desmond Julian in Edinburgh articulated the concept of the coronary care unit where patients could be continuously monitored and have complications promptly treated; mortality immediately fell by half and these units subsequently spread quickly; DRI was not long behind in having its own unit housed in a side-ward off one of the main medical wards.

Such was the strength of Professor Ian Hill's cardiology department that he was able to attract national and international delegates to teaching symposia and courses. Here are participants in one of these events at DRI in 1962. Professor Hill is seated centre front, Dr Ken Lowe is two along to the left, and Drs Donald Emslie-Smith and Hamish Watson are three and four along on the right.

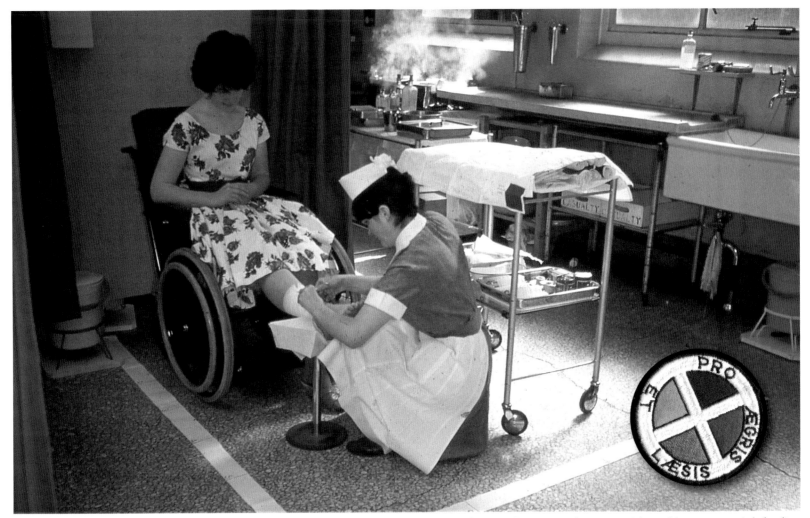

This DRI scarf badge (bottom right) shows the four colours of state-registered nurse uniform in the 1960s to be worn with a white apron – pink for first year students, lilac for second and third year students (the latter had an extra stripe on the arm), light blue for staff nurse and dark blue for ward sister. State-enrolled nurses wore a green uniform. Everything became white in the 1970s other than the hats which had coloured stripes to denote grade, with ward sisters wearing a frilly cap. Shown above is a 'pinkie' doing a leg dressing in 1961.

All nurses who completed their three-year training followed by a further year working at DRI received a bronze medal (left). Silver medals (right) were given to ward sisters. The 'most deserving nurse' of the year was awarded the Ogilvy Dalgleish gold medal for all-round excellence, founded by Sir William Ogilvy Dalgleish, President of DRI 1890-1913.

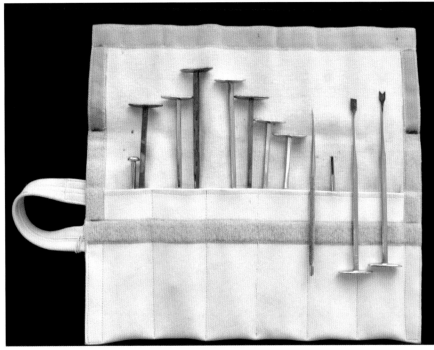

These knives were used for cutting out torn knee cartilages, and were designed by Dundee's first Professor of Orthopaedic Surgery, Ian Smillie. He was a world authority on injuries and diseases of the knee joint, wrote classic monographs on both and was a brilliant surgical technician and innovator, his knives being used throughout the world. On one occasion, however, an arch-rival (whom we shall call Mr X) attacked the famous knives by saying "the only use for which I can recommend Mr Smillie's knives is to sharpen pencils"; the audience was astonished when Smillie claimed to agree with the attacker, but then went on to say "the best possible use Mr X can make of these knives *is* to sharpen pencils!"

These photographs show a heart valve replacement being conducted at DRI in the mid-1960s. Dundee was only the second city in the UK to undertake this procedure (known as open heart surgery), which involves the use of a machine to take over the heart's pumping action. These were exciting times, not least in West Theatre where the leading American heart surgeon Michael DeBakey operated at the invitation of Donald Douglas. Douglas had become Professor of Surgery in 1951 and was meticulous in his work, expecting the same high standards from his team to whom he was an inspiring teacher. Former trainee Michael Lyall describes watching his operations as "just like turning the pages of a book". In 1965, Douglas and his surgical colleague William F Walker reported their experience of 401 operations for rheumatic disease of the mitral and aortic valves and 251 for congenital heart disease. In time, dwindling numbers of suitable patients and the need to centralise expertise for more complex recurrent cases led to heart operations ceasing in DRI just before transfer to Ninewells in 1974.

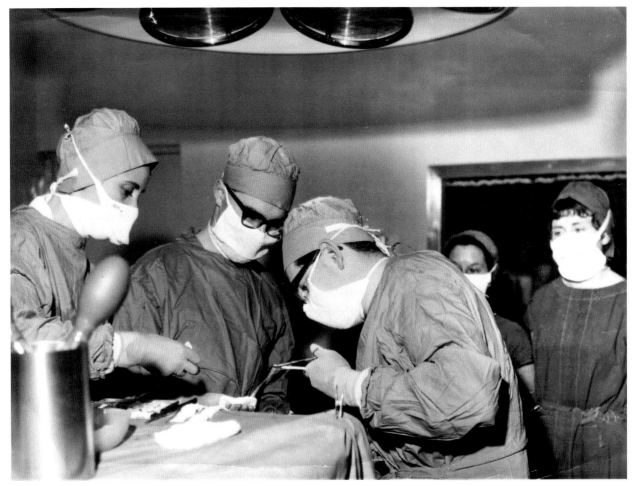

A dedicated department of surgical neurology was opened at DRI in 1966 by the South Africans Joseph Block and Ivan Jacobson. Block had arrived in 1962, with no ward, no dedicated beds, no theatre and no dedicated theatre nurse. However, through a combination of exceptional skills and inspirational care the two men developed their fledgling unit into a service that became second to none; Jacobson was Dundee Citizen of the Year in 1984 and was awarded the OBE for services to medicine. Their big thinking was typified by a 1982 campaign to raise £60,000 for a Cavitron machine, the appeal being met in true Tayside fashion within just a few weeks to allow removal of a spinal tumour from young Brian Sweeney. In 1988, surgeon TRK Varma was the first in Scotland to use stereotactic surgery to treat deep-seated brain tumours. Seen here is an early action shot from theatre.

There was always a great sense of loyalty and camaraderie amongst DRI staff and reunions like the one seen here were a frequent occurrence, particularly amongst the nurses. The most frequent questions asked would have been "do you remember…?" and "what happened to nurse so-and-so?".

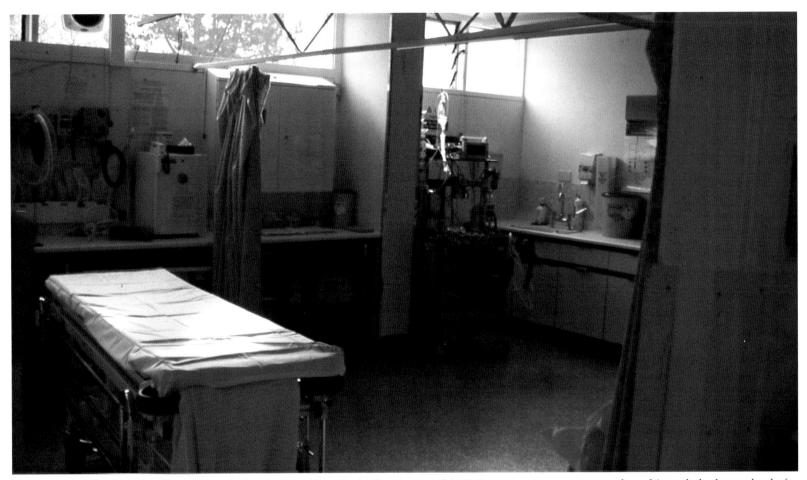

The one-storey Accident and Emergency department at the front of DRI was erected in 1964 as a temporary measure, but ultimately had to make do for 34 years! The photograph here shows the resuscitation room to where the most seriously ill were taken. By the 1990s it was apparent that having an A&E department physically separated from supporting specialities was no longer tenable. This split site in Dundee was singled out for particular criticism in reports that showed that trauma care throughout the UK was substandard. Once the decision to move to Ninewells Hospital was made, clinical staff were fully involved in the planning, design and equipping of the new unit. By the time of the move in 1998 there were clear policies in place for how the new combined unit would function and integrate with the services already on the Ninewells site. One week after closure, A&E staff held a final party in the shell of the DRI department and bade farewell to the old 'Casualty'!

Christmas was always a happy time at DRI, and not only for the children! Parties were held throughout the hospital with plenty of good sustenance, and the nurses went carolling around the wards to cheer up those who had to spend the festive season as in-patients.

In the 1920s, 70% of Dundee's births took place at home, but most births now take place in hospital following a fierce debate in the 1960s. This photograph from 1974 shows the last baby born at DRI held by Ellena Salariya (left), and the first baby born at Ninewells Hospital held by Sheila Brown (right), surrounded by a happy group of nurses.

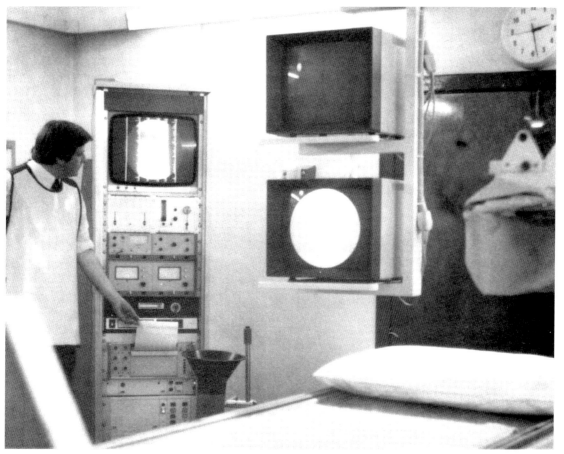

Until 1977, urological surgery in Tayside was carried out by general surgeons. In that year the Board appointed Keith Baxby as an accredited specialist urological surgeon at DRI to develop a centralised service there. Urology occupied two wards and the original main operating theatre. Considerable investment in equipment and staff was needed to bring the speciality up to date. The Board provided state-of-the-art urodynamic equipment in 1979, and in the early 1980s charitable and Board funding provided the equipment for percutaneous ('keyhole') surgery on the kidney. The department developed an in-house teaching programme for registrars and in 1989 introduced kidney transplantation to Tayside. The move of Urology to the Ninewells site, planned and promised for 1981, eventually took place in 1998. By that time the department had four consultants and the training programme for registrars had expanded to involve rotation with Aberdeen, Dunfermline and Edinburgh. This picture shows Keith Baxby with specialised equipment for studying bladder disorders.

John Kirk was the Tayside region's first plastic surgeon in 1960, based at Bridge of Earn Hospital with an additional four adult and six children's beds at DRI. The opening of Ninewells Hospital in 1974 allowed for expansion and modification of the facilities in Ward 4 at DRI. Close links were established between the plastic surgeons with dental and oral surgery colleagues, and in 1986 a new, greatly enlarged, Regional Plastic Surgery Centre was opened at the vacated maternity unit covering three floors, incorporating a dedicated Burn Unit and Theatre representing the highest standards in burns facilities at the time. Seen here is a Padgett Dermatome used to cut thin slices of skin for grafting.

The bone pins and forceps seen here were used at DRI's orthopaedic unit. There were two orthopaedic theatres, one for elective cases (i.e. non-emergency procedures, scheduled in advance) and the other for acute trauma and semi-elective cases; a long day in the former might well be followed by a long night in the latter. These long hard hours were made easier by a sense of togetherness and sharing. This was best exemplified by Christmas dinner in Ward 14 when the turkey was dissected by the surgeon into plate-sized portions to the enthusiastic anticipation of the twenty or so patients; this was followed by the doctors and nurses doing a Strip the Willow up and down the length of the ward. A real community!

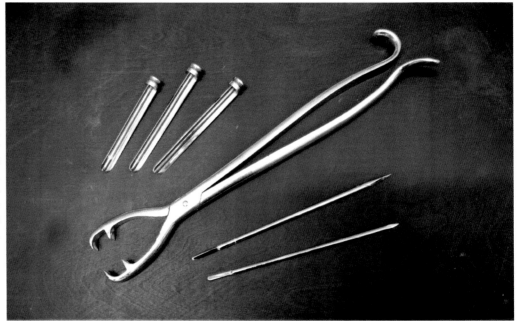

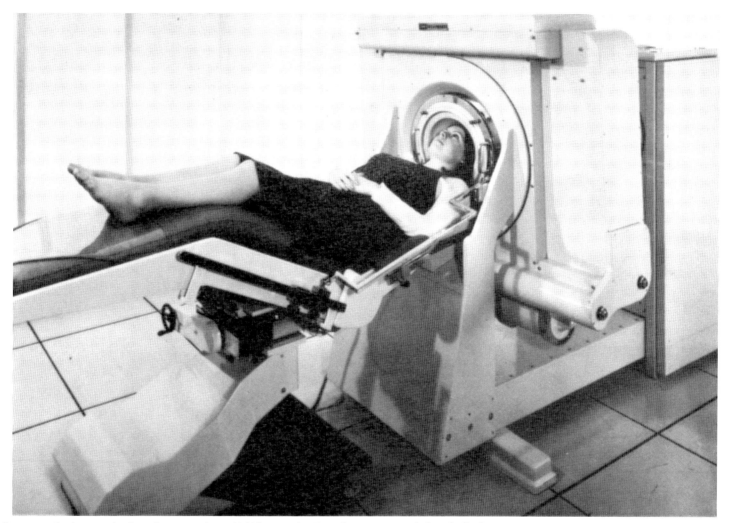

DRI's first neurologist was Andrew Lenman; from 1960 he ran the Tayside service single-handedly for many years. By 1993 the department had expanded to three consultants and had office, secretarial and research accommodation distributed over four different locations in the Infirmary, but moved that year to a fifteen-room suite of refurbished offices and laboratories centred on Ward 10 to complement an MRI scanner gifted by the government and a CAT scanner that had come from public subscription in 1976. The latter was one of the earliest in the UK and is shown here.

The porters at DRI did far more than simply ferrying patients around the hospital in beds or chairs. They were also responsible for delivery of meals, pharmacy items and CSSD packs, delivery and uplift of mail, transfer of specimens to laboratories and cadavers to the mortuary, uplift of dirty linen and sharps boxes, removal of refuse and glass and changing of medical gases. They were also always at the ready to help out in the A&E department. Here is a happy group in front of the west door, where they were stationed.

After Ninewells opened, DRI served as the trauma centre for Dundee and so, despite taking place on Ninewells' doorstep, it was to DRI that 53 casualties of the 1979 Invergowrie train crash were ferried by ambulance and taxi, twelve of these being detained. Five people were killed in this accident which took place very close to the location and to the centenary of the 1879 Tay Bridge Disaster. However, it was clear that it made no sense to have acute medicine, general surgery and intensive care on one site and accident and emergency, neurosurgery, orthopaedics, oral surgery and plastic surgery on another. In 1998 the remaining DRI departments moved to Ninewells and the buildings were put up for sale.

Shortly before DRI closed a special event was held to give staff a chance to get together and reminisce about old times. It took place in the Boardroom, and was organised by the late Laura Adam, seen in the centre of this photograph. Laura was the first Curator of the Tayside Medical History Museum, and she made valiant efforts to track down much of the material that is in this book.

Scattered around DRI were a number of plaques commemorating much-loved members of staff and benefactors of the Infirmary. These are now on permanent display at Ninewells Hospital in the main concourse, one of various displays organised by the Tayside Medical History Museum which exists to promote the story of medical care throughout the region. Further information can be found at www.dundee.ac.uk/museum/medical.htm